C
E
Mur

GOD CARES WHEN THINGS ARE NOT OKAY

Three stories for children based on favorite Bible verses

ELSPETH CAMPBELL MURPHY
ILLUSTRATED BY JANE E. NELSON

This Guideposts edition is published by special arrangement with Chariot Books, David C. Cook Publishing Co.

GOD CARES WHEN I'M DISAPPOINTED
© 1983 Elspeth Campbell Murphy for the text and Jane E. Nelson for the illustrations.
GOD CARES WHEN I'M WONDERING
© 1984 Elspeth Campbell Murphy for the text and Jane E. Nelson for the illustrations.
GOD CARES WHEN I DON'T FEEL GOOD
© 1987 Elspeth Campbell Murphy for the text and Jane E. Nelson for the illustrations.

Scripture quotations from the The Holy Bible, New International Version.
Copyright © 1973, 1978, 1984 International Bible Society. Used by permission of Zondervan Bible Publishers.

Printed in the United States of America.

Guideposts®
Carmel, New York 10512

GOD CARES WHEN I'M DISAPPOINTED

BY ELSPETH CAMPBELL MURPHY
ILLUSTRATED BY JANE E. NELSON

"For I know the plans I have for you,"
declares the Lord,
"plans to prosper you and
not to harm you,
plans to give you hope and a future."

Jeremiah 29:11, NIV

We're having a parade today, God.
But I didn't get picked to be in it!

My brother plays the drum in the band.
Boom chick-chick. Boom chick-chick.
Boom chicka-chick-chick. BOOM! BOOM!

But marching in the band was not what I wanted to do.

Yesterday I helped my sister decorate her bike
with bright, swirly crepe paper.
"It's too bad only the big kids
are riding their bikes this year," she said.

But riding my bike was not what I wanted to do.

I wanted to be the princess!

The princess of the parade gets to wear
a beautiful, long cape and a diamond crown,
and she gets to ride on a throne
and throw candy to all the kids.

I was sure I would get to be the princess because I wanted to so much.
But they picked somebody else!
And now all I get to do is stand on the curb
and watch the parade go past.
I think to myself,
"Nothing nice will ever happen to me again."

That's how it feels when you're disappointed.

But you know what, God?
Maybe being princess of the parade
isn't the most important thing in the world after all.

I mean, a parade doesn't last forever—
just a couple of hours.
Then it's all over,
and a person is not a princess anymore.

But do you know what is more exciting
than being a princess, God?
It's having you for my friend forever,
and ever,
and ever!

Even if I didn't get to be the princess,
I'm still special and important to you.
You listen when I talk to you.
I can always tell you when I'm sad or disappointed about something.

You seem to have a secret just for me.
And you give me the sureness of your Word:

"For I know the plans I have for you,"
declares the Lord,
"plans to prosper you and not to harm you,
plans to give you hope and a future."

Jeremiah 29: 11

I can find this verse on page _____
in my Bible.

*This text is taken from the New International Version, but you may use the version of your choice.

GOD CARES WHEN I'M WONDERING

BY ELSPETH CAMPBELL MURPHY
ILLUSTRATED BY JANE E. NELSON

He has also set eternity
in the hearts of men;
yet they cannot fathom what
God has done from beginning
to end.

Ecclesiastes 3:11b, NIV

You know what, God?
Sometimes my friends and I
play a game that goes like this:
"If you could be any animal for a day,
what would you be?"
And I always say,
"A bird! I would be a bird!"
I love the birds you made, God.

One time my mother and I
went to a place called an aviary
at the zoo.
I thought it was hot and steamy,
and my mother said that's because
the birds in there
came from hot, steamy jungles—
and the zoo keepers wanted them to feel at home.

AVIAR

LITTER

And ever since then, God,
I've wondered about those faraway jungles
where no people live.
I've wondered about those beautiful,
bright-colored birds,

flying through the trees
with no one to see them . . .
parrots and cockatoos and toucans—
just being there
because you made them.
I like to think about that.

I wonder about a lot of things, God.
Sometimes the questions inside me
are like popcorn, pop-pop-popping in my head.
How come worms taste good to birds?
What's happening when my stomach hurts?
What if I *ever* get *really* sick?
Why do bad things have to happen?
What's it like in heaven?
How come sometimes you break a bone
when you fall and sometimes you don't?
How come birds are able to fly, but not people?

You know what, God?
I think birds fly
because you put the flying in them.
And I think I wonder about things
because you put the wondering in me.

For our science fair
I'm going to do a project on birds.
But you know what I figured out, God?
Even if I were an ornithologist
and learned EVERYTHING
there is to know about birds,
I still wouldn't know what it feels like
to *be* a bird.

I will never know what it feels like
to fly, and fly, and fly. . . .

That's just the way it is with wondering, God.
There are some questions I can get the answers to.
And there are some questions I can't.
Like, I can read a book to find out
how many kinds of birds there are.
But no one knows *why* there are so many kinds.
Only you know that.

Only you know why the world needed
hummingbirds and ostriches
and so many kinds of sparrows.
Only you know if you had fun
making penguins.

I love finding out about your world, God.
I love thinking about things—
even though I'll never find all the answers.
That's just the way it is with people, isn't it, God?
They will always wonder and wonder.
But it's different for you—
because you're the one who *knows*.

a. crown
b. throat
c. breast
d. wing bars
e. tail

SCIENCE FAIR

We'll go on wondering.
And that's okay,
because in your Word it says
that our wondering
comes from you.

He has also set eternity
in the hearts of men;
yet they cannot fathom what
God has done from beginning
to end.

Ecclesiastes 3:11 b*

This verse is found on page____in my Bible.

*This text is taken from the New International Version, but
you may use the version of your choice.

GOD CARES WHEN I DON'T FEEL GOOD

BY ELSPETH CAMPBELL MURPHY
ILLUSTRATED BY JANE E. NELSON

"My grace is all you need,
for my power is strongest
when you are weak."

II Corinthians 12:9a, NIV

Last night I got really sick, God!
And I was so scared,
because I didn't know what was wrong.

My throat still feels
all hot and red inside.
It hurts to swallow!
Most of the time—
when I'm well—
I don't even think about having a thr⟨o⟩
But now my throat feels bigger and s⟨o⟩
than any other part of me.

And my skin feels hot and dry and tight—
like it doesn't fit the way it should.
My mother says it feels that way
because I have a fever.

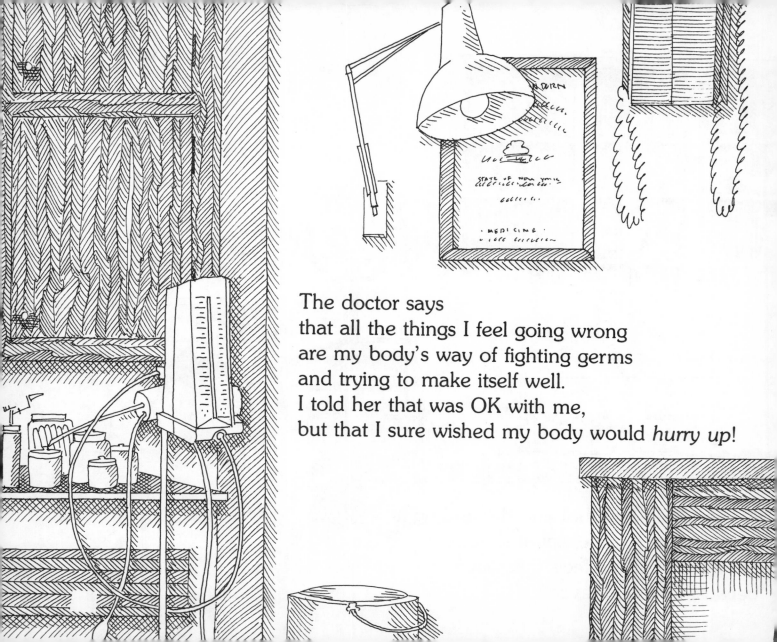

The doctor says
that all the things I feel going wrong
are my body's way of fighting germs
and trying to make itself well.
I told her that was OK with me,
but that I sure wished my body would *hurry up*!

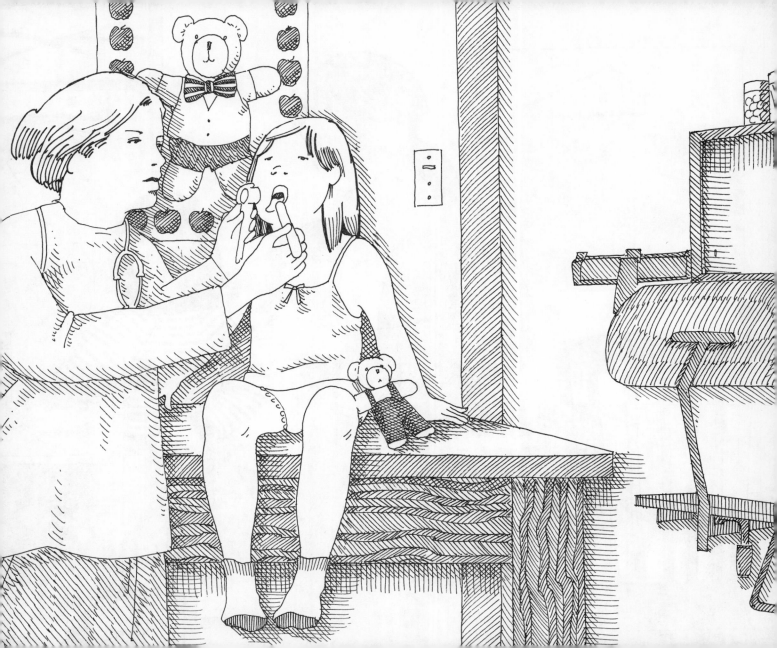

The doctor says
I need to rest
so the medicine can go to work
and so my body can use all its energy
to make itself better.

I don't like resting.
I want things to be
just the way they usually are.
Usually I can get up
and DO stuff.
I don't like being sick, God!

My mother told me
to take a little nap.
But I couldn't sleep,
and I felt so worn out
I started to cry.

So then she wrapped me up in a comforter
and held me
and rocked me
and called me her poor, sweet baby.

That might seem funny,
because I'm not a baby anymore.
But we didn't laugh,
because it sounded just right.
My mother held me close,
and she helped me to rest.

And you know what, God?
I think that's the way *you* are, too!
Because you understand
that sometimes people just get tired
and weak
and sick.

But you are always taking care of us.
And when we're all worn out and scared,
it's like you pick us up
and rock us in your arms
and say to us,
"I'm holding you.
Just rest, just rest."

You are all we need, God,
because you are the strongest One there is.

That's why you say in your Word:

"My grace is all you need, for my power is strongest when you are weak."
* II Corinthians 12:9a

This verse is found on page____ in my Bible.